Stories for 2 Year Olds

Stories for 2 Year Olds

LITTLE TIGER PRESS
London

Contents

It's Mine!

Ewa Lipniacka   Jane Massey

"It's mine!" yelled Jack.

"Mine!" screamed Georgie.

"It belongs to nobody now
you've broken it," scolded Mum.
"You two must learn to share!"

In the garden Georgie shared
her favourite worm with Jack.

And Jack shared his biggest
mud pies with Georgie.

Jack shared Georgie's
teddy with the dog.

And Georgie shared Jack's pencils
with the children next door.

At dinner Jack shared
his peas with Georgie.

And Georgie shared
her dinner with the cat.

Georgie shared her
bath with Jack.

And Jack shared his scariest
bedtime story with Georgie.

They both tried to
share Georgie's bed.

Then Jack began to scratch
and itch and scritch and scratch.

"Chicken-pox," said Mum,

and put him to bed.

And then Georgie began to scratch
and itch and scritch and scratch.

"Do you two have to share
everything?" asked Mum.
"Yes!" they said together.
"Especially YOU!"

Come Join in the Fun!

Hello! Hello!

Hello! Hello!

Come down below,

It's lovely and cool

Out here in the pool;

On a lily-pad float

For a nice green boat.

Here we sit and sing

In a pleasant ring;

Or leap frog play,

In the jolliest way.

Our games have begun,

Come join in the fun.

~ Louisa May Alcott

Making Music!

Banging on my drum-drum,
Jingling my bell.
Here's a tooty trumpet —
You can play as well!

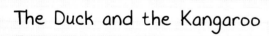

The Duck and the Kangaroo

Said the Duck to the Kangaroo,
"Good gracious! How you hop!
Over the fields and the water too,
As if you never would stop!"

~ Edward Lear

Dance with Me

Come join the circle and dance with me,
dance with me, dance with me.
Come join the circle and dance with me,
Then shake your shoulders and pat your knee.

Come jump in puddles and splash with me,
splash with me, splash with me.
Come jump in puddles and splash with me,
Then waddle home   it's time for our tea!

Messy Play

What fun, little one,
On a painting spree.
Who's a messy baby,
Happy as can be!

Tumbling

In jumping and tumbling
We spend the whole day,
Till night by arriving
Has finished our play.
What then? One and all,
There's no more to be said,
As we tumbled all day,
So we tumble to bed.

What Bear Likes Best!

Alison Ritchie

Dubravka Kolanovic

Bear was sunning himself on his
favourite hilltop. He loved days
like this — nothing in particular to do
and nowhere in particular to go.

Buzzzzzzzzzz!

Buzzzz! A bee
landed on his nose.

34

"Get up, Bear," he said crossly.

"How can I collect pollen with bears
squashing my flowers?"

"Sorry, Bee," said Bear, laughing.

Bear curled himself up
and roly-polied down the hill.
Roly-polying was one of his
favourite things to do.

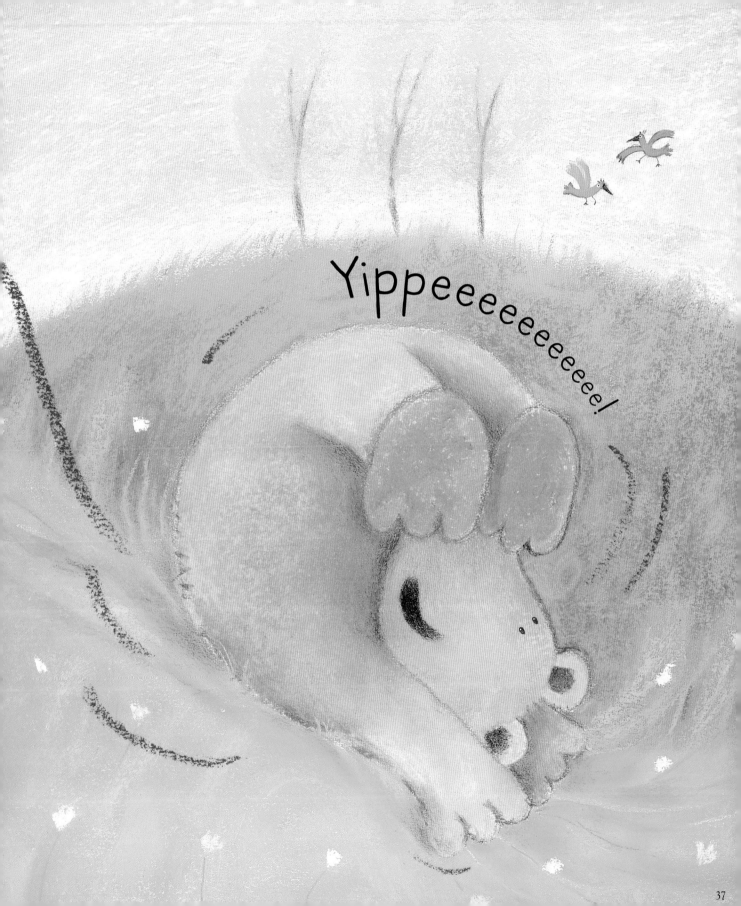

Bump! Bear landed on top
of something warm and furry.
"Oi!" gasped Mole. "How can I
dig holes with bears landing on me?"

Ooooof!

"I'll help you!" said Bear. And he dug
and dug and dug.

"Stop! Stop! STOP!" cried Mole,
as mud flew everywhere.

"Sorry, Mole," said Bear and
he hurried away.

Bear ran towards the river
and splashed into the water.
Splashing was one of his
favourite things to do.

Splish!

Splash!

"Hey!" grumbled Heron. "How can I catch fish with bears chasing them away?"

"Sorry, Heron," said Bear and he bounced off to play somewhere else.

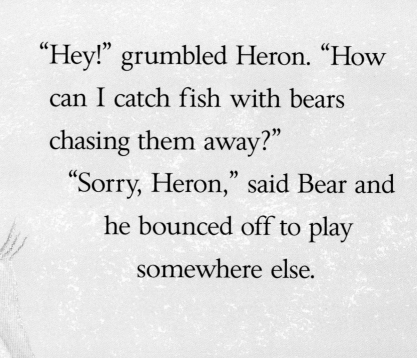

Blah!

Bear hopped across the stepping stones,
leaped onto the riverbank and ran into
the woods. It was time for a back scratch.
Scratching his back was one of his
favourite things to do.

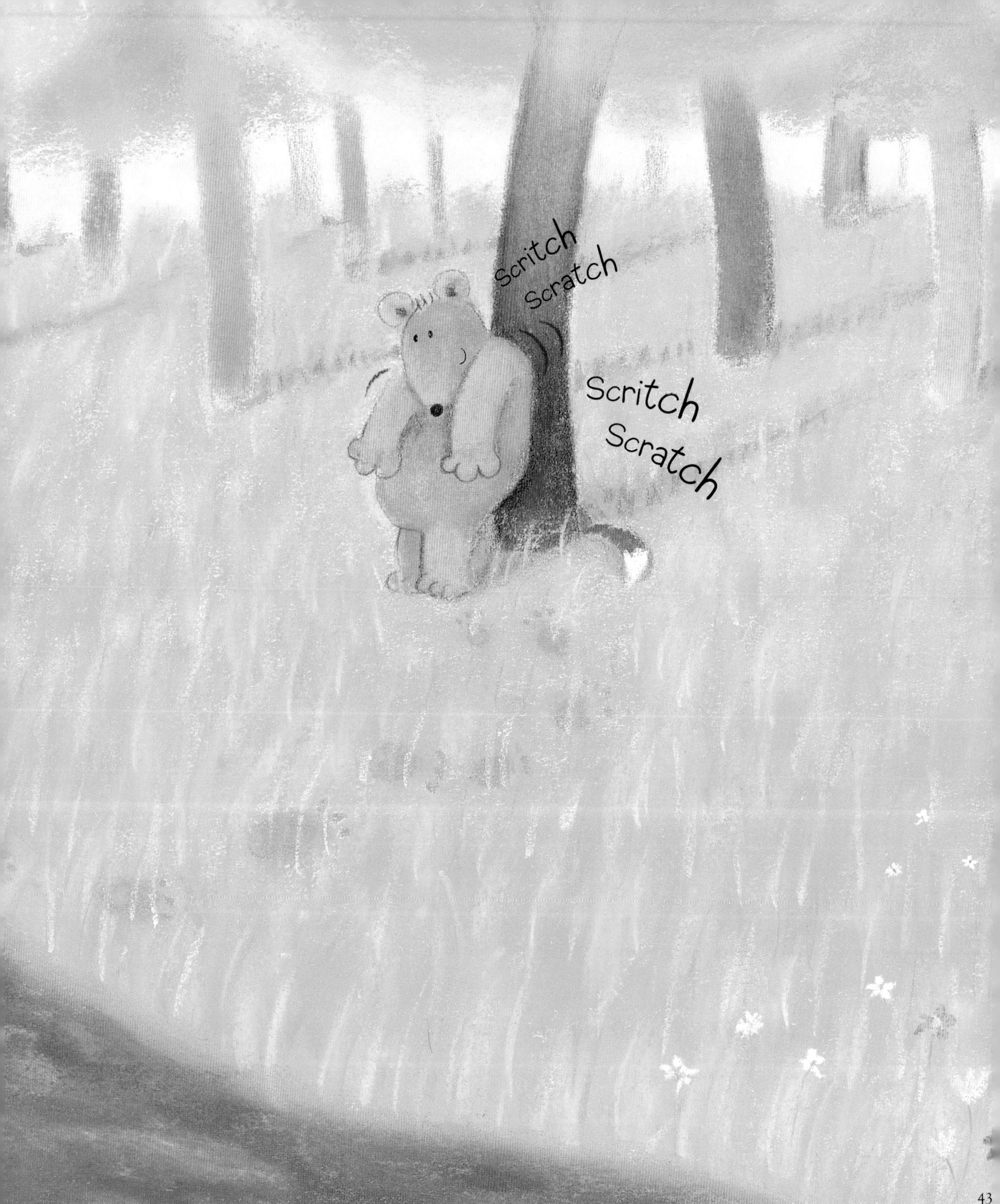
Scritch
Scratch
Scritch
Scratch

"Who's that?" said Fox, sleepily.
"How can I rest with bears
shaking the trees?"

"Sorry, Fox," said Bear.
"Do you want to scratch
too? It's so nice!"
    But Fox did not
want to scratch,
so Bear clambered
up the tree.

45

Bear swung from branch to branch.
Swinging was one of his favourite
things to do.

Ooops!

Crash! Bear flew into a tree trunk.

"Yikes!" cried Woodpecker, flying high into the air. "How can I peck holes with bears crashing into my tree?"

"Oops! Sorry!" cried Bear, jumping to the ground.

"Bother! Everyone's too busy to play," Bear thought. "Oh well!" He skipped through the woods, along the riverbank, across the field and back to his favourite hilltop.

La, la la, la la!

Bear lay sunning himself on the hilltop.

Suddenly he heard a loud BUZZZZZZZ!
"Oh no! I'm in trouble again," he thought.

He saw all his friends coming towards him.

"Bear," said Bee, "you're very big . . ."

"And heavy," said Mole.

"And noisy," said Heron.

"And pesky," said Fox.

"And clumsy," said Woodpecker . . .

. . . "But you're really fun.
   Let's play!"

"Hoorah!" cried Bear.
Because playing with his friends
really *was* his favourite thing to do.

You Are Two, and I Love You

Days With You

Let's build a castle in the sand
And dance around it, hand in hand.
Days with you are so much fun -
Let's play again, my little one!

You're My Star

You're my star.
You're my light.
Oh, the joy that you bring!
You're my day.
You're my night.
You're my everything.

What Shall I Do Today?

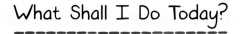

What shall I do with this pile of leaves?
Jump! Jump! Jump!
What shall I do on these woodland trees?
Climb! Climb! Climb!

What shall I do to this tower of bricks?
Wibble! Wobble! Topple!
What shall I do with this drum and sticks?
Bash! Bang! Bash!

What shall I do in this cosy bed,
Snuggled up tight with my cuddly ted?
What shall I do when you close the door?
Shhhhh! Listen . . .
Snore! Snore! Snore!

Hoppity Skip, Little Chick

Jo Brown

Little Chick bounced out of
bed one bright sunny morning.
"Let's play, Mum!"
he chirped.

"I need to keep these eggs
safe and warm just a little while
longer, Little Chick," said Mum,
"but I'm sure you'll find someone
to play with in the farmyard."

Little Chick tottered
outside and looked around.
Just then some geese rushed past.
"Honk honk! Follow us!"
they cried.

whiz

ZZZZZ!

Little Chick thought
that running looked fun.
So he ran too!

Little Chick tootled along —
quite fast for a little chick.

whoOooosh!

Faster and faster he ran, so fast his little chick
legs got tangled up and he tripped . . .

yeeeeEEEK!

. . . and skidded
into a lamb!
"Meeerrrr!"
said the lamb.
"That looks like fun,
but why don't you
try this?"

And she bounced
around.

boing!
merrr!
merrr!

Little Chick thought
that bouncing looked fun.
So he bounced too!

BOING! Little Chick managed
a little bounce. Well, quite a big
bounce for a little chick.

He bounced . . .

and he bounced . . .

and he bounced.

He bounced so high that he whizzed through the air . . .

peeyungggg!

. . . right into a pony!

"Oops!" said the pony. "Nice bouncing, Little Chick, now why don't you jump over this fence with me?"

And the pony jumped
straight over the fence.

Yeee-haa!

Little Chick thought
that jumping looked fun.
So he jumped too!

Little Chick did a little jump . . . then he did a bigger jump.

Then he did a REALLY
BIG jump, right over the
fence into the next field . . .

Splonggg!

. . . and landed right
on top of a piglet!

"Oops, sorry!" said Little Chick. "I need more practice landing, but jumping is great fun!"

Kersplatt!

"If you think that's fun, try this. It's luuuverly!" said the piglet, and he rolled around in the mud.

"What fun!"
thought Little Chick.
So he scritched and
he scratched . . .

and then he had
a little bit of a roll . . .

and then he did a wiggly
dusty chick dance until there
was dust everywhere.

aaaachooo!

"This is the best
fun of all!" he cried.

"Great rolling, Little Chick!" said the piglet.

"I'm having so much fun today!" said Little Chick.
"All this bouncy-jumpy-roly-running!
I can't wait to tell my mum.
See you later, Piggy!"

And he rushed
across the farmyard
to the hen house . . .

... where he had a HUGE surprise!

"Hello, Little Chick," said Mum.
"Here are your new brothers
and sisters."

"**yippee-aye-aayyy!**"
yelled Little Chick.
"Now we can all play
together!"

83

And they played bouncy-jumpy-
roly-running little chick games,
all day long! And it was the
greatest fun EVER!

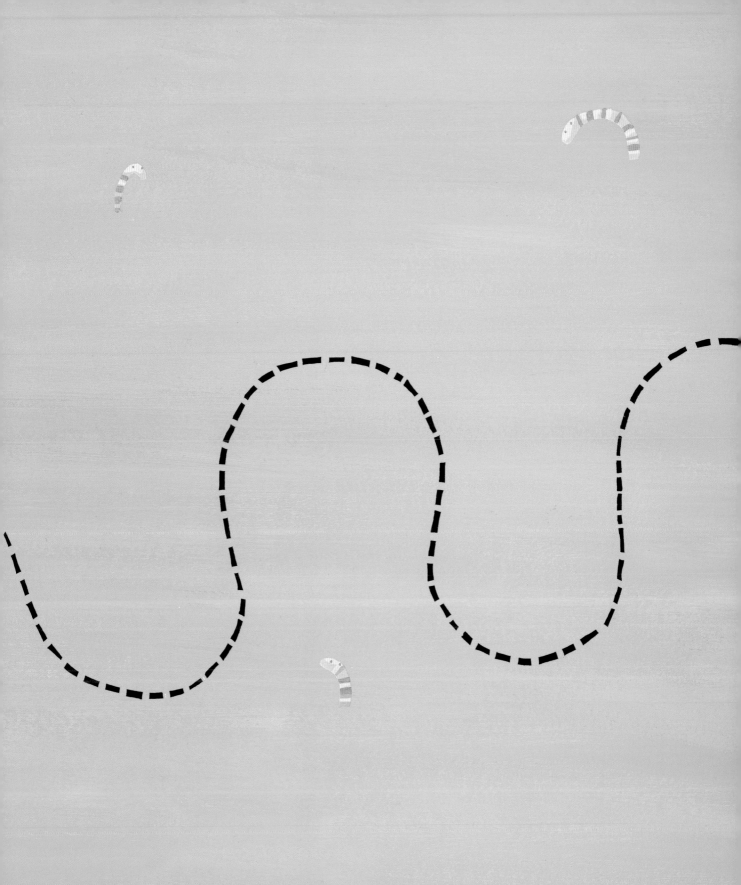

Outdoor Play

Bubble Wand

How hard it is to squeeze my lips

Into a tiny 'o'.

And even when I've worked it out,

I still forget to blow!

So now I have a different way

To make my bubbles fly:

I hold my wand above my head

And wave it in the sky.

Boats Sail on the Rivers

Boats sail on the rivers,

And ships sail on the seas;

But clouds that sail across the sky

Are prettier far than these.

~ Christina Rossetti

If All the World Were Paper

If all the world were paper,

And all the sea were ink,

If all the trees were bread and cheese,

What would we do for drink?

The Balloon Man

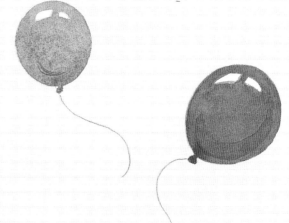

He always comes on market days,
And holds balloons — a lovely bunch —
And in the market square he stays,
And never seems to think of lunch.

They're red and purple, blue and green,
And when it is a sunny day
Tho' carts and people get between
You see them shining far away.

And some are big and some are small,
All tied together with a string,
And if there is a wind at all
They tug and tug like anything.

Some day perhaps he'll let them go
And we shall see them sailing high,
And stand and watch them from below —
They would look pretty in the sky.

~ Rose Fyleman

Mo's
SMELLY JUMPER

David Bedford

Edward Eaves

Mo Monkey always
wore his rainbow jumper.

He wore it when he collected juicy
berries with Mother Monkey . . .

And he wore it when he made
mud pies with his friends, Ellie and Tig.

Mo used his jumper to clean his
hands and feet before dinner . . .

And to wipe his face afterwards.

One day Mother Monkey said, "That jumper is dirty.
It smells and pongs and whiffs. I'm going to wash it."

And she pulled the jumper
right over Mo's head!

But Mo wouldn't let go.

Mother Tiger and Tig strolled by.

"Why are you pulling on Mo's
rainbow jumper?" asked Mother Tiger.

"It smells and pongs and whiffs," said Mother Monkey.
"I want to wash it but Mo won't let go. Help me pull."

Mother Tiger helped pull.

But Tig and Mo pulled the other way.

Mother Elephant and Ellie stopped to watch.

"Why is everyone pulling on Mo's rainbow jumper?"

asked Mother Elephant.

"It smells and pongs and whiffs," puffed Mother Monkey.
"I want to wash it but Mo won't let go. Help me pull."

Mother Elephant helped pull.

But Ellie, Tig and Mo pulled the other way.

"Pull!" shouted the mothers.

"Pull!" shouted Ellie, Tig and Mo.

Mo whispered to his friends.
"One, two, three . . ."

"LET GO!"

Mother Elephant, Mother Tiger
and Mother Monkey all fell backwards.
They rolled and tumbled through the mud
and landed in a heap. Mo, Ellie and Tig laughed.
"Now you all need a wash," giggled Mo.

While the three mothers had a bath, Mo washed
the jumper himself until he could see the
bright rainbow colours again.

Then he hung it up to dry in the sun.

But when Mo put his jumper back on, it hung
all the way down to his feet . . .

"Oh no!" cried Mother Monkey. "We've stretched
your rainbow jumper!"
"Don't worry," said Mo. "My jumper is
even better now because . . ."

"I can *sleep* in it as well!"

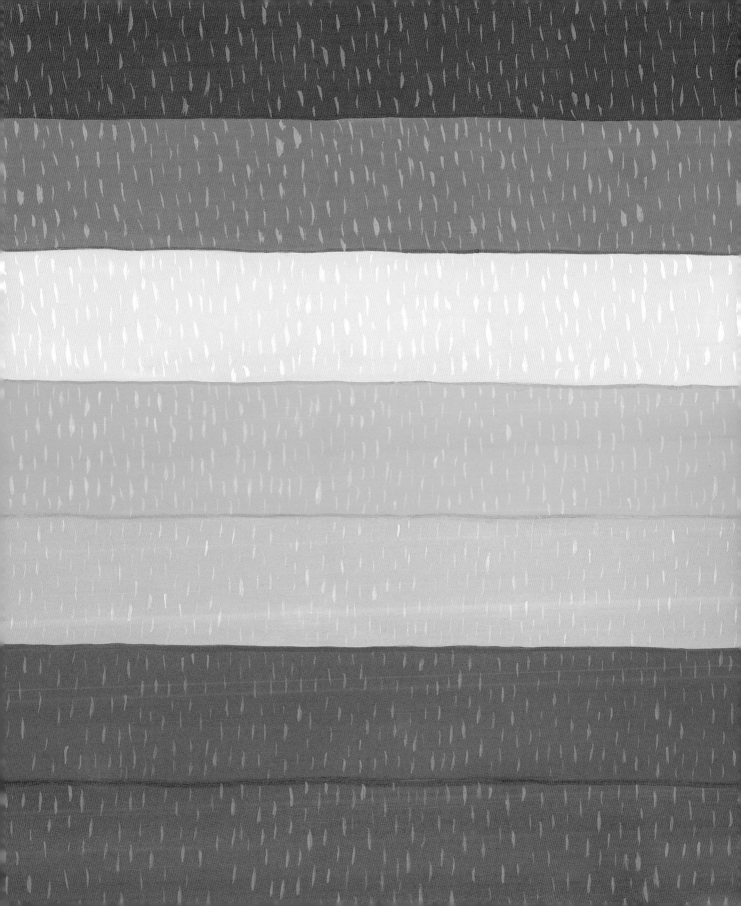

All Year Round

Bread and Milk for Breakfast

Bread and milk for breakfast,
And woollen frocks to wear,
And a crumb for robin redbreast
On the cold days of the year.

~ Christina Rossetti

Snowflake

Catch a snowflake on your tongue
And it sparkles,
And it shivers,
And it tingles,
And it quivers,
And then, in a breath, it is gone.

Ted's Pants

"Don't put pants on your head,"
said Mummy to Ted,
And she started to simmer and scold.
"But my legs were too hot,"
said Ted, "so why not?"
"And my ears were a wee bit too cold."

Lolly-Lolly, Little Lamb

Lolly-Lully, Little Lamb
She makes muffins,
topped with jam.
Are you hungry?
"Oh, yes I am!"
says Lolly-Lolly, Little Lamb.

Bathtime, PiggyWiggy

Diane and Christyan Fox

Sometimes when I have my bath, I close my eyes and think of all the things that I could be

in the water...

I could be
a deep-sea
diver...

searching for
sunken treasure!

Or maybe a waterskier...

flying high above the waves!

Or even a long-distance swimmer...

dodging a giant
sea monster.

Or perhaps I could be a lifeboat pilot...

speeding through

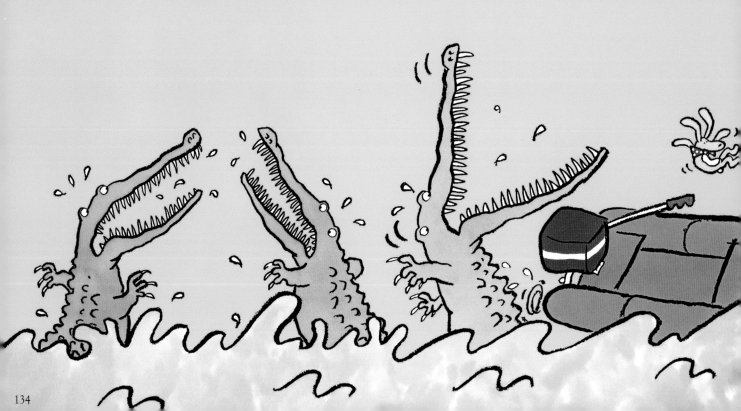

the water ...

to rescue
my friends.

Better still,
a champion surfer,
riding the top of the
biggest waves . . .

and whooshing
down again!

Best of all
I'd like to
sail a boat...

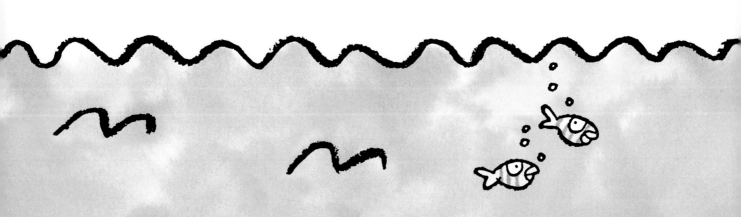

. . . around
the world
with all
my friends.

And when my journey's done,
I'll sail right home again!

I wonder who
I'll be tomorrow?

Time for Bed, Sleepyhead!

Bonnie Girls and Bonnie Boys

Bonnie girls and bonnie boys,
Picking up their bonnie toys.
No more play, it's time for bed,
Time to rest their bonnie heads!

My Little Baby

While you sleep,
The world spins round,
Slowly to rock you,
Safe and sound.
The morning will come,
A new day will break.
And my little baby,
From dreams will awake.

146

Five in the Bed

There were five in the bed, and the little one said,

"Roll over! Roll over!"

So they all rolled over, and one fell out . . .

There were four in the bed, and the little one said,

"Roll over! Roll over!"

So they all rolled over, and one fell out . . .

There were three in the bed, and the little one said,

"Roll over! Roll over!"

So they all rolled over, and one fell out . . .

There were two in the bed, and the little one said,

"Roll over! Roll over!"

So they all rolled over, and one fell out . . .

There was one in the bed, and the little one said,

"Goodnight! Goodnight!"

Books for Baby

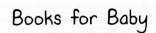

Let's read about a pirate

or sing a nursery rhyme.

Let's wake a scary dragon

and just escape in time!

Let's choose a fairy tale

then a book about the zoo.

I LOVE these precious stories

and sharing them with you!

When the Sun Goes Down to Bed

When the sun goes down to bed,
The stars come out to play.
They dance across the sky all night,
Until the break of day.

Fairy Song

The moonlight fades from flower and rose
And the stars dim one by one;
The tale is told, the song is sung,
And the Fairy feast is done.

~ Louisa May Alcott

A Kiss for
Little Kitten

Claire Freedman

Caroline Pedler

My mummy wakes me with a kiss,
Just like she does each day.
I've had a lovely, snuggly sleep,
But now it's time to play!

I scamper down the garden path.

I wonder what I'll see?

Oh, look! A great, big grasshopper

Is jumping out at me!

I like to climb my favourite tree
And try to reach the top.
Oh dear, this branch is really high —
I think that I should stop!

Hooray! I've found the perfect place
For me to stop and hide.
But, oh, this big, old watering can
Has water still inside!

"It's rest time now," calls Mummy,
So we stretch out in the sun.
I tell her my adventures.
I've been having so much fun!

There's something twitching in the grass.
I'm following its trail.
So, ready, steady, go – then pounce!
Oh no! It's Mummy's tail!

It's bathtime! Mummy washes me.
I try hard not to wriggle.
"But, Mummy, when you lick my fur,
It tickles me!" I giggle.

I'm clean and bathed and happy,
And there's still time left to play.
I dance among the shadows,
While an owl hoots far away.

"It's beddy-byes now," Mummy says.
"The stars are twinkling bright.
Let's cuddle up, my little one,
And wish the moon goodnight!"

STORIES FOR 2 YEAR OLDS

LITTLE TIGER PRESS
1 The Coda Centre
189 Munster Road
London SW6 6AW
www.littletiger.co.uk

First published in Great Britain 2013

Printed in China

LTP/1800/0931/0514

ISBN 978-1-84895-729-9

4 6 8 10 9 7 5 3

IT'S MINE!

WHAT BEAR LIKES BEST!

HOPPITY SKIP, LITTLE CHICK

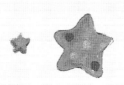

ACKNOWLEDGEMENTS

'Bonnie Girls and Bonnie Boys', 'My Little Baby', 'When the Sun Goes Down to Bed'
by Stephanie Stansbie, copyright © Little Tiger Press 2008;
'Making Music', 'Dance with Me', 'Messy Play', 'You're My Star', 'What Shall I Do Today?',
'Bubble Wand', 'Books for Baby' by Stephanie Stansbie, copyright © Little Tiger Press 2013;
'Snowflake', 'Ted's Pants', 'Lolly-Lolly, Little Lamb' by Mara Alperin, copyright © Little Tiger Press 2013

Additional artwork by Rachel Baines, copyright © Little Tiger Press 2010, 2013

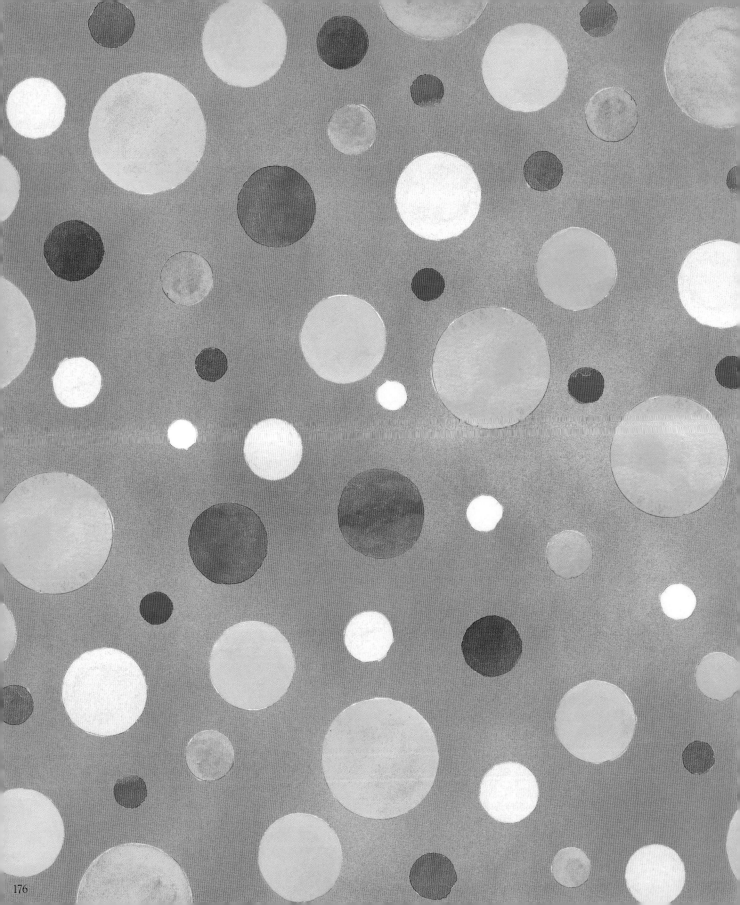